Audition Son for Male Singers 3

Angels...

plus nine more hit songs
ideal for auditions

Wise Publications
London/New York/Paris/Sydney/Copenhagen/Berlin/Madrid/Tokyo

Exclusive Distributors:
Music Sales Limited
8/9 Frith Street,
London W1D 3JB, England.
Music Sales Pty Limited
120 Rothschild Avenue,
Rosebery, NSW 2018,
Australia.

Order No. AM972400
ISBN 0-7119-9146-4
This book © Copyright 2002 by Wise Publications

Music arranged and performed by Paul Honey.
Music processed by Enigma Music Production Services.

CD recorded, mixed and mastered by Jonas Persson.

Cover photograph (Robbie Williams) courtesy of Rex Features.

Printed in the United Kingdom by
Printwise (Haverhill) Limited, Suffolk.

Angels

Words & Music by Robbie Williams & Guy Chambers

Moderately

I sit and wait,___

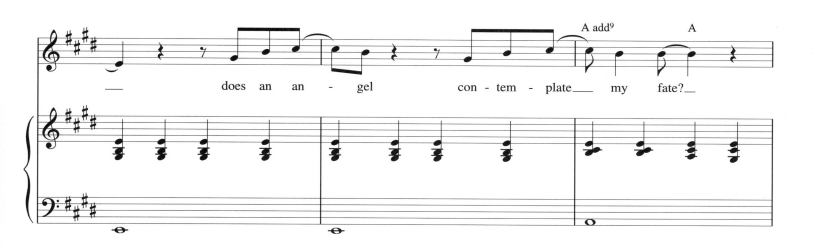

___ does an an - gel con - tem - plate___ my fate?___

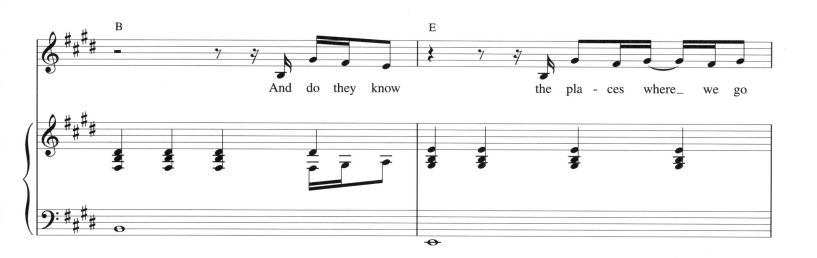

And do they know the pla - ces where_ we go

when we're grey and old?____ 'Cause I have been__

told that sal - va - tion lets their wings__ un - fold,__

So when I'm ly - ing in my bed thoughts

run - ning through my head and I feel that love is dead,__

I'll al - ways be blessed_ with love._ And
as the feel - ing grows she brings flesh to my bones and
when love is dead, I'm lov - ing an - gels in - stead.
And through it all_

10

Come What May

Words & Music by David Baerwald

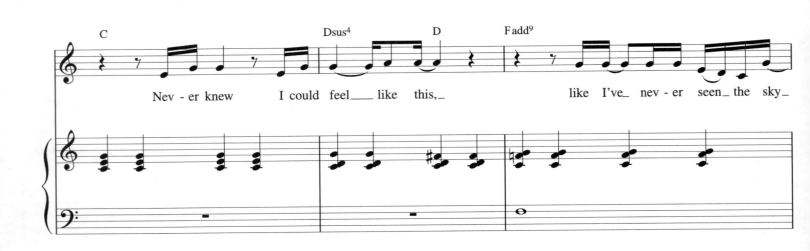

Nev - er knew I could feel___ like this,_ like I've_ nev - er seen_ the sky_

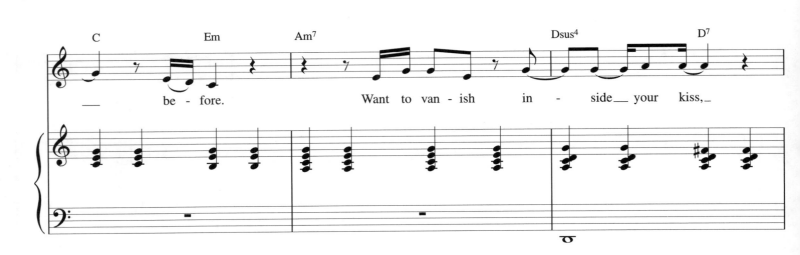

___ be - fore. Want to van - ish in - side___ your kiss,_

Is You Is Or Is You Ain't My Baby?

Words & Music by Billy Austin & Louis Jordan

The Music Of The Night

Music by Andrew Lloyd Webber
Lyrics by Charles Hart
Additional Lyrics by Richard Stilgoe

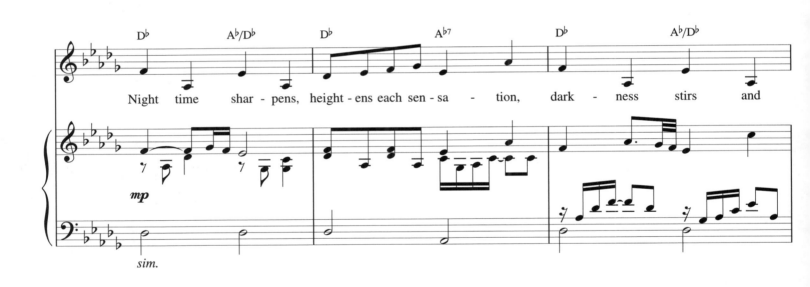

Night time shar - pens, height - ens each sen - sa - tion, dark - ness stirs and

wakes i - ma - gi - na - tion, si - lent - ly the sen - ses a-

-fore! Close your eyes let your spi - rit start to soar and you'll

live as you've nev - er lived be - fore.

Soft - ly, deft - ly, mu - sic shall ca - ress you,

hear it, feel it, se - cret - ly pos - sess you.

meno mosso

be.
On - ly then can you be - long to me.

Float - ing, fall - ing, sweet in - tox - i - ca - tion, touch me, trust me,

sa - vour each sen - sa - tion, let the dream be - gin, let your dark - er side give in to the

pow - er of the mu - sic that I write, the pow - er of the mus - ic of the

No Matter What

Music by Andrew Lloyd Webber
Words by Jim Steinman

Gentle beat

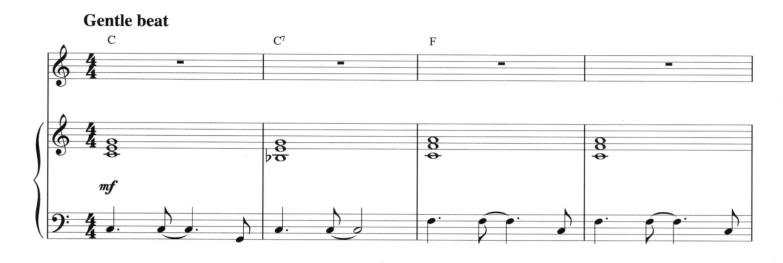

No mat - ter what they tell us,   no mat - ter what they do,
(Verse 2 see block lyric)

I know our love's for - ev - er, I know no mat - ter what._____

No mat - ter who they fol - low, no mat - ter where they

lead,   no mat - ter how they judge us,   I'll be ev - 'ry - one you need.__

__ No mat - ter if__ the sun__ don't shine,_____ or if the__ skies are blue.__

__ No mat - ter what the end - ing,   my life be - gan   with

you.   I can't de - ny___ what I_____ be - lieve,__

I can't be___ what I'm not.___   I know this love's for - ev - er. That's all that

mat - ters now no mat - ter what.   No no mat - ter what.

No no mat - ter what._____   No no mat - ter what.

Verse 2:
If only tears were laughter, if only night were day,
If only prayers were answered, then we would hear God say.
No matter what they tell you, no matter what they do,
No matter what they teach you, what you believe is true.
And I will keep you safe and strong and sheltered from the storm.
No matter where it's barren our dream is being born.

Reet Petite

Words & Music by Tyran Carlo & Berry Gordy Jr.

ev - er seen a girl for whom your soul you'd give, for whom you'd fight for, die for, pray_
(Verse 2 see block lyric)

F⁷ ... B♭⁷
— to God you'd lie for, she's so_____ fine, ___ she's

F⁶ ... C⁷
so_____ fine, _____ she's real - ly sweet, the fi - nest

B♭⁷ ... F⁶
girl you'd ev - er wan - na meet. Well_ she real - ly

oh, oh, oh, oh, oh, oh,

Rrr - rr - reet Pe - tite, the fi - nest girl you ev - er wan - na meet.

D. 𝄋 al Coda

Well __ she's like

Verse 2:
Well, she's like honey from a bee,
And like bees from a tree
I love her, need her, she beez so buzzin,
She's alright, she's got what it takes, she's got what it takes and to me she really rates
Well oh, now she's my cutey, my tutti frutti,
My heart, my love, my bathin' beauty, she's alright,
She's just got what it takes, she's got what it takes and to me she really rates.

Oh, oh, oh, oh, *etc.*

Shoes Upon The Table

Words & Music by Willy Russell

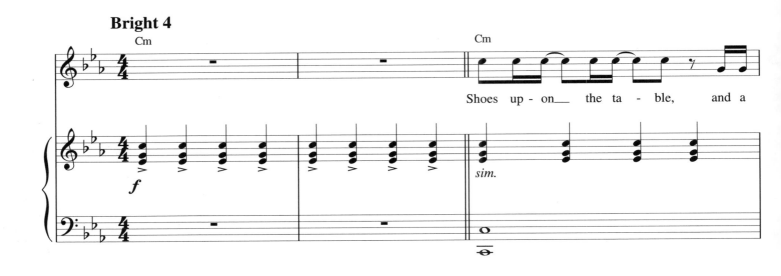

Shoes up-on the ta-ble, and a

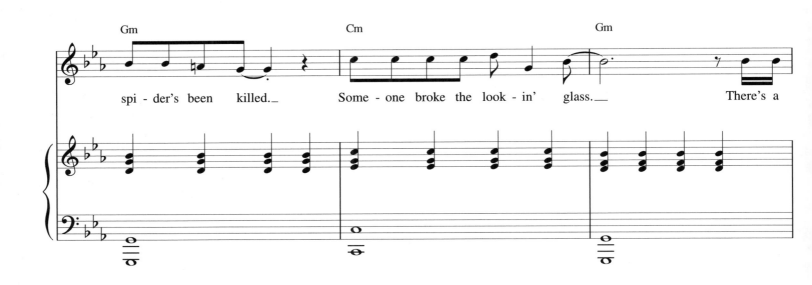

spi-der's been killed. Some-one broke the look-in' glass. There's a

full moon shi-nin' and the salt's been spilled.

B♭ F/A Cm E♭
know the de - vil's got your num - ber. You know he's gon - na find
F E♭ F E♭
you, you know he's right be - hind you, he's stan-
F D7/F♯ Cm F D7/F♯
- din' on your step and he's knock - in' at your door. He knock - in' at your door,
rall.
Cm F D7/F♯ Cm
he's knock - in' at your door.

Try A Little Tenderness

Words & Music by Harry Woods, Jimmy Campbell & Reg Connelly

She may be wea-ry,   wo-men do get wea-ry

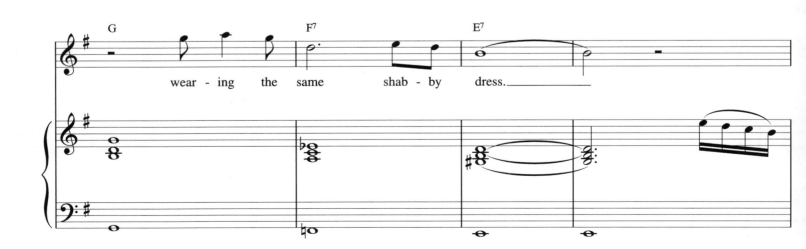

wear-ing the same shab-by dress.

word_____ that's soft and gen - tle_____ makes it ea - si - er_____ to bear._____ You won't re - gret it,___ wo - men don't for - get it,___ love is their whole hap - pi - ness._____

It's all so ea - sy, try a lit - tle ten - der -

- ness.___ You've got to

squeeze her, don't tease her, nev - er___ leave her,

try a lit - tle ten - der - ness.

Your Song

Words & Music by Elton John & Bernie Taupin

And you can tell ev - 'ry - bo - dy   this is your song,_

it may be quite sim - ple but   now that it's done._

I hope you don't mind,   I hope you don't mind   that I put down in

words   how won - der - ful life___ is   now

This Year's Love

Words & Music by David Gray

Slow

1. This year's love had bet-ter last;___ hea-ven knows, it's high

2. Turn-ing cir-cles and time a-gain___ it cuts___ like a knife.___ Oh now,

if you love me I got to know for sure.___

'Cause it takes some-thing more this time___ than sweet,___ sweet___ lies,___ oh now,

be-fore I op-en up my arms and fall, los-ing all con-trol, ev-'ry
(Verse 3 see block lyric)

Verse 3:
'Cause who's to worry if our hearts get torn
When that hurt gets thrown?
Don't you know this life goes on?
Won't you kiss me on that midnight street
Sweep me off my feet
Singing ain't this life so sweet?

Other great book & CD song collections for auditions...

Audition Songs for Female Singers 1
Don't Cry For Me Argentina...
plus Adelaide's Lament, Big Spender; Heaven Help My Heart;
I Cain't Say No; I Will Survive; Out Here On My Own; Saving All My Love For You;
Someone To Watch Over Me; The Wind Beneath My Wings. ORDER NO. AM92587

Audition Songs for Female Singers 2
I Dreamed A Dream...
plus Another Suitcase In Another Hall; Fame; If I Were A Bell; Miss Byrd;
Save The Best For Last; Someone Else's Story; There Are Worse Things I Could Do;
What I Did For Love; You Can Always Count On Me. ORDER NO. AM950224

Audition Songs for Female Singers 3
Memory...
plus Can't Help Lovin' Dat Man; Crazy; Diamonds Are A Girl's Best Friend;
Now That I've Seen Her; Show Me Heaven; That Ole Devil Called Love;
The Winner Takes It All; Wishing You Were Somehow Here Again;
The Reason. ORDER NO. AM955284

Audition Songs for Female Singers 4
I Don't Know How To Love Him...
plus As Long As He Needs Me; Constant Craving; Feeling Good;
I Say A Little Prayer; If My Friends Could See Me Now;
It's Oh So Quiet; Killing Me Softly With His Song; Tell Me It's Not True;
You Must Love Me. ORDER NO. AM955295

Audition Songs for Female Singers 5
Chart Hits
Against All Odds (Take A Look At Me Now); American Pie; ...Baby One More Time;
Breathless; It Feels So Good; Man! I Feel Like A Woman; My Love Is Your Love;
Pure Shores; Rise; Sing It Back. ORDER NO. AM963765

Audition Songs for Female Singers 6
90's Hits
History Repeating; I Will Always Love You; Never Ever; Perfect Moment;
Search For The Hero; That Don't Impress Me Much; Torn; 2 Become 1;
What Can I Do; You Gotta Be. ORDER NO. AM963776

Audition Songs for Male Singers 1
Tonight...
plus All Good Gifts; Anthem; Being Alive; Corner Of The Sky; Funny;
High Flying, Adored; If I Loved You; Luck Be A Lady;
Why, God, Why? ORDER NO. AM92586

Audition Songs for Male Singers 2
Maria...
plus All I Need Is The Girl; Bring Him Home; Frederick's Aria;
I Don't Remember Christmas; Sit Down, You're Rocking The Boat;
Some Enchanted Evening; This Is The Moment; Where I Want To Be;
You're Nothing Without Me. ORDER NO. AM950213

Audition Songs for Male & Female Singers
Gilbert & Sullivan
I Am The Very Model Of A Modern Major-General; I'm Called Little Buttercup;
The Nightmare Song (When You're Lying Awake With A Dismal Headache);
On A Tree By A River (Willow, Tit Willow); Poor Wand'ring One!;
Silvered Is The Raven Hair; The Sun Whose Rays Are All Ablaze;
Take A Pair Of Sparkling Eyes; When All Night A Chap Remains;
When Maiden Loves She Sits And Sighs. ORDER NO. AM958188

Audition Songs for Male & Female Singers
Christmas Hits
Fairytale Of New York; Happy Xmas (War Is Over);
I Wish It Could Be Christmas Every Day; Last Christmas; Lonely This Christmas;
Merry Xmas Everybody; Mistletoe And Wine; A Spaceman Came Travelling;
Step Into Christmas; Wonderful Christmastime. ORDER NO. AM971586

Audition Songs for Kids
Any Dream Will Do; Consider Yourself; I'd Do Anything; No Matter What;
Spice Up Your Life; Thank You For The Music; The Candy Man; Tomorrow;
When I'm Sixty Four. ORDER NO. AM955273

ALL TITLES AVAILABLE FROM GOOD MUSIC RETAILERS OR, IN CASE OF DIFFICULTY, CONTACT
MUSIC SALES LIMITED, NEWMARKET ROAD, BURY ST. EDMUNDS, SUFFOLK IP33 3YB
TELEPHONE: 01284 725725; FAX: 01284 702592
WWW.MUSICSALES.COM

To remove your CD from the plastic sleeve, lift the small
lip on the right to break the perforated flap.
Replace the disc after use for convenient storage.

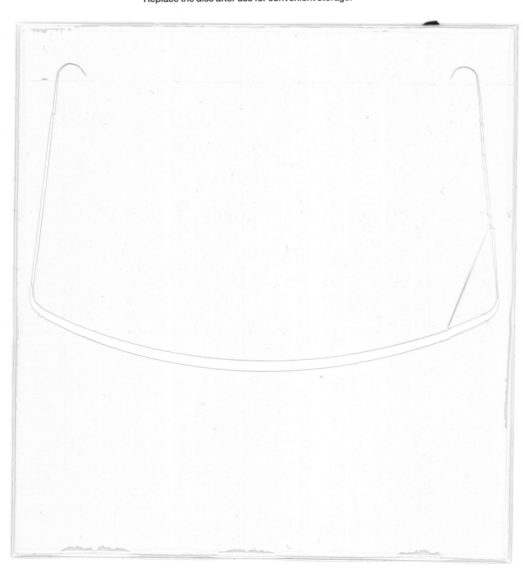